It Takes Two
10 GREAT POP DUETS

Published by
Wise Publications
14-15 Berners Street, London W1T 3LJ, UK.

Exclusive Distributors:
Music Sales Limited
Distribution Centre, Newmarket Road,
Bury St Edmunds, Suffolk IP33 3YB, UK.
Music Sales Pty Limited
120 Rothschild Avenue, Rosebery, NSW 2018, Australia.

Order No. AM984643
ISBN 13: 978-1-84609-327-2
ISBN 10: 1-84609-327-9
This book © Copyright 2007 Wise Publications,
a division of Music Sales Limited.

Compiled by Nick Crispin.
Music arranged by Paul Honey.
Music processed by Paul Ewers Music Design.
Designed & art directed by Michael Bell Design.
Illustrated by Angela Dundee.
Printed in the EU.

CD recorded, mixed & mastered by
Jonas Perrson & John Rose.
Backing tracks arranged by Danny G.
Vocals by Alison Symons, Alexander Troy, John Williams,
Jo-NasT & Cathryn Hopkins.

Your Guarantee of Quality:
As publishers, we strive to produce
every book to the highest commercial standards.
The music has been freshly engraved and the book has been
carefully designed to minimise awkward page turns
and to make playing from it a real pleasure.
Particular care has been given to specifying acid-free,
neutral-sized paper made from pulps which have not been
elemental chlorine bleached.
This pulp is from farmed sustainable forests and was
produced with special regard for the environment.
Throughout, the printing and binding have been planned
to ensure a sturdy, attractive publication which
should give years of enjoyment.
If your copy fails to meet our high standards,
please inform us and we will gladly replace it.

www.musicroom.com

WISE PUBLICATIONS
part of The Music Sales Group

London / New York / Paris / Sydney / Copenhagen / Berlin / Madrid / Tokyo

The Ballad Of Tom Jones

Words & Music by Thomas Scott, Francis Griffiths & James Edwards

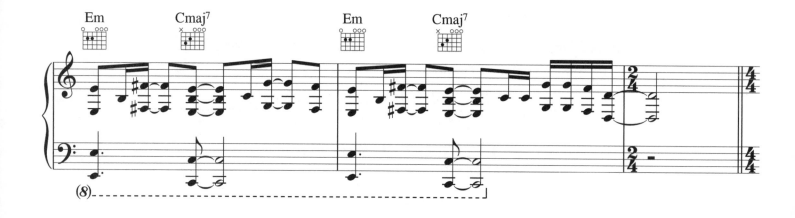

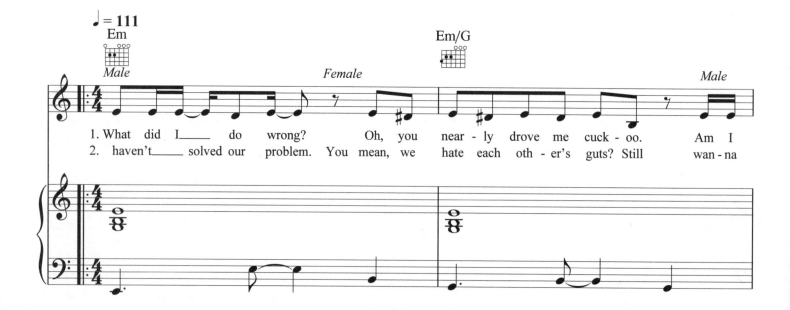

1. What did I ___ do wrong? Oh, you near-ly drove me cuck-oo. Am I
2. haven't ___ solved our problem. You mean, we hate each oth-er's guts? Still wan-na

Don't Go Breaking My Heart

Words & Music by Ann Orson & Carte Blanche

Don't go break-ing my heart._____

I won't go break-ing your heart..

Don't go break-ing my heart.____

Don't Know Much

Words by Cynthia Weil
Music by Barry Mann & Tom Snow

and that may be ___ all I ___ need ___ to know.

and that may be ___ all I ___ need ___ to know.

So ma-ny ques-tions still left un-an-swered,

so much I've ___ nev-er brok-en through. ___

Especially For You

Words & Music by Mike Stock, Matt Aitken & Pete Waterman

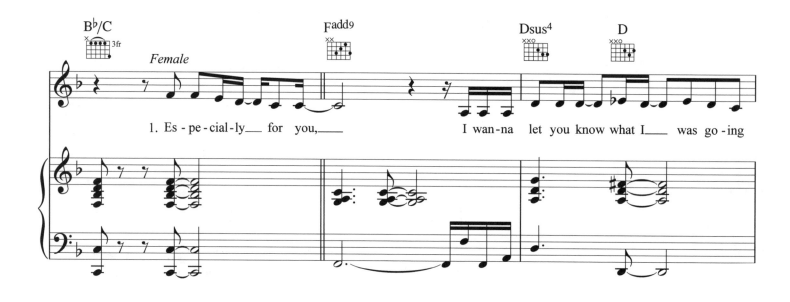

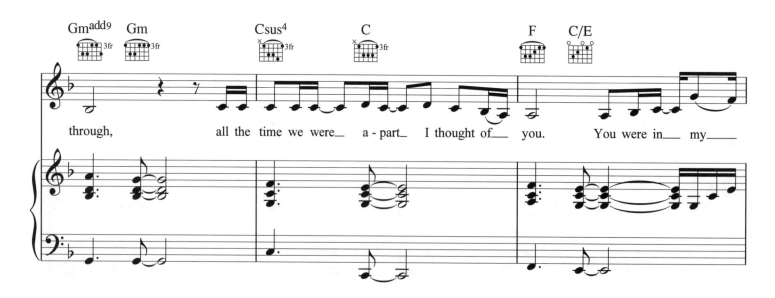

24

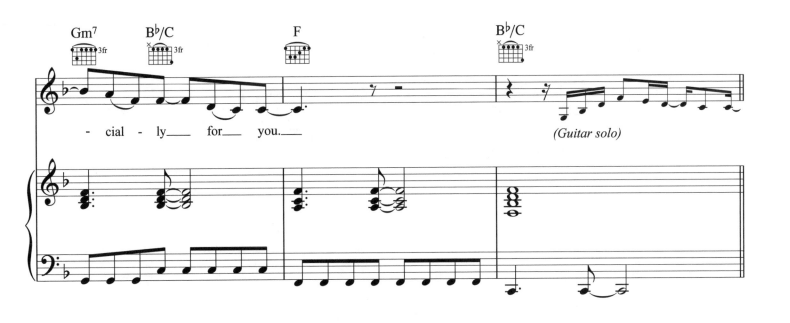

- cial - ly___ for___ you.___

(Guitar solo)

Female

You were in___ my___ heart,   my love nev - er changed.___

D.S. al Coda

I Knew You Were Waiting (For Me)

Words & Music by Simon Climie & Dennis Morgan

con - sumed by the sha - dows. I was crip - pled e - mo - tion - 'lly.
the hurt__ is ov - er; one touch__ and you set__ me free.

Male

Mmm.__
No.__

Some - how I made it through the
I don't re - gret a sin - gle

Female (2°) *Male*

heart - aches,__ yes I did;__ I es - caped.__
mo - ment,__ no I don't.__ I know you don't. Look - ing back,__

I found my way out of the dark - ness.__ I kept my faith,__
when I think of all these dis - ap - point - ments,__ I just laugh,__

31

Islands In The Stream

Words & Music by Barry Gibb, Maurice Gibb & Robin Gibb

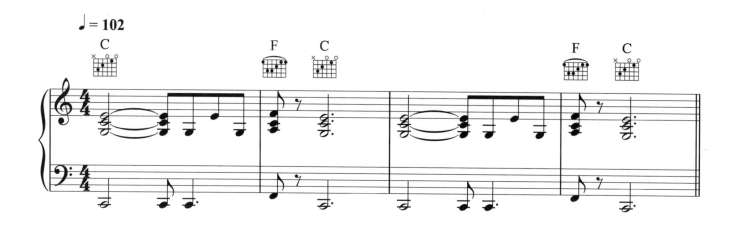

Male

Ba - by, when I met you there was peace un - known, I set out to get you with a fine tooth-comb. I was

soft in - side, there was some-thing go - ing on.

got no - one, and you___ did walk in to - night

slow -

- ly los - ing sight of the real___ thing.___

Female

But

Male

But

that won't hap - pen to us, and we got no doubt,___ too deep in love and we got

that won't hap - pen to us, and we got no doubt, too deep in love and we got

A Little Time

Words & Music by Paul Heaton & David Rotheray

time___ to find my free - dom.___ I need a lit - tle...
room___ all___ a - lone___ I need a lit - tle... You
time___ and I still love_ you__ I've had a lit - tle... You

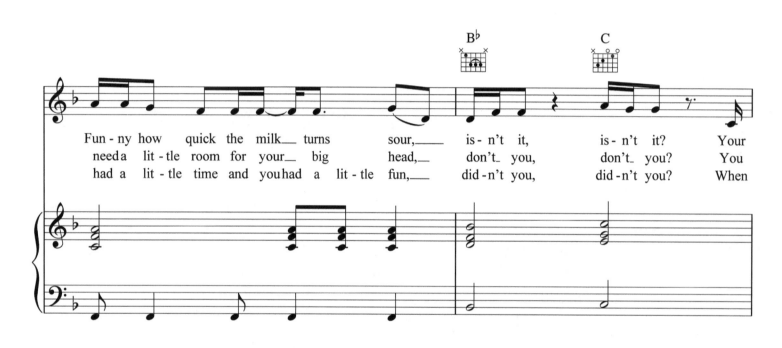

Bb C

Fun - ny how quick the milk__ turns sour,___ is - n't it, is - n't it? Your
need a lit - tle room for your_ big head,___ don't_ you, don't_ you? You
had a lit - tle time and you had a lit - tle fun,___ did - n't you, did - n't you? When

F Bb

face has been look - ing like that for hours,____ has - n't it, has - n't it?
need a lit - tle space for a thou - sand beds,____ won't you, won't you?
you had yours do you think I had none,____ do_ you do_ you? The

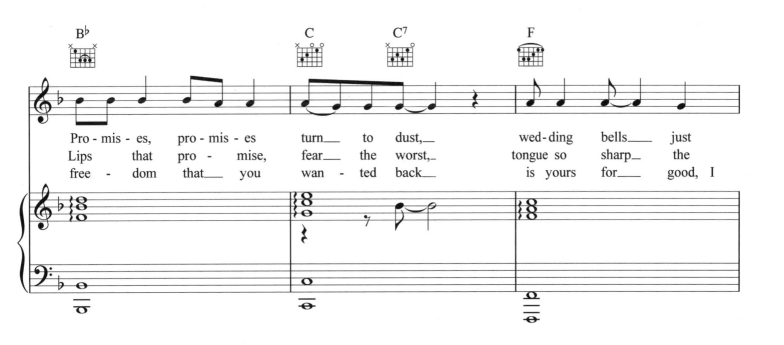

Pro - mis - es, pro - mis - es turn__ to dust,__ wed - ding bells__ just
Lips that pro - mise, fear__ the worst,__ tongue so sharp__ the
free - dom that__ you wan - ted back__ is yours for__ good, I

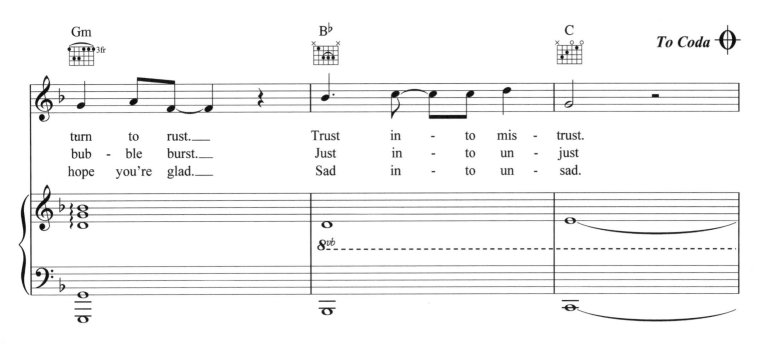

turn to rust.__ Trust in - to mis - trust.
bub - ble burst.__ Just in - to un - just
hope you're glad.__ Sad in - to un - sad.

To Coda ⊕

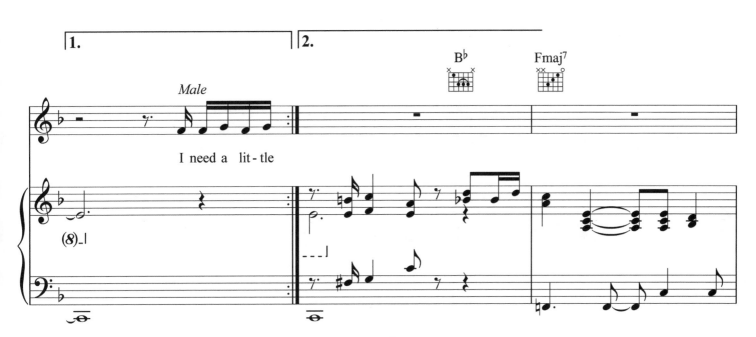

1.

2.

Male

I need a lit - tle

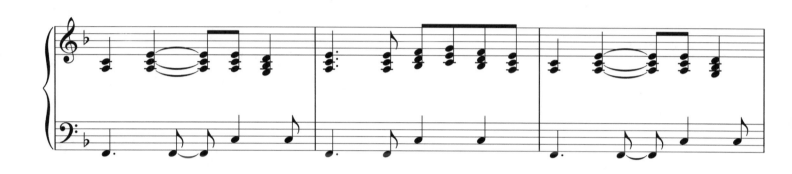

D.S. al Coda

Male

I need a lit-tle

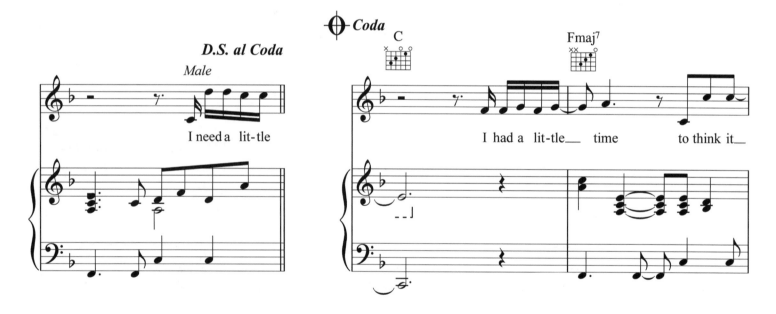

⊕ *Coda*

C

Fmaj⁷

I had a lit-tle___ time   to think it___

___ ov - er.___   Had a lit-tle___ room___   to work_ it   out.___   I found a lit-tle___

Kids

Words & Music by Robbie Williams & Guy Chambers

On My Own

Words & Music by Carole Bayer Sager & Burt Bacharach

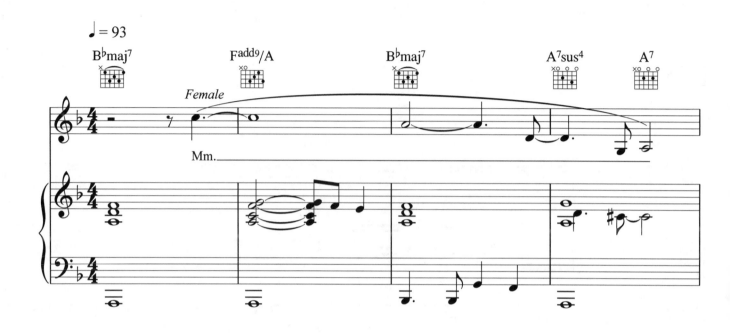

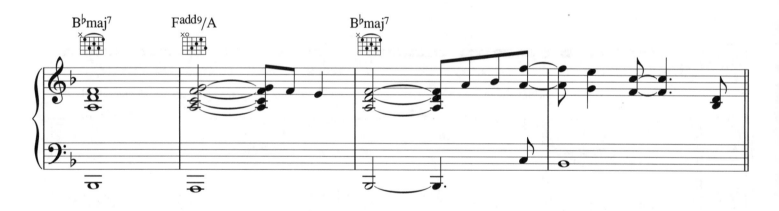

So ma-ny times said it was____ for-ev-er,

said our love would al - ways be true,_____ some-thing in my heart al-ways

knew I'd be ly - ing here be-side you:_____ On my own,_____

on my own,_____ on my own.__

Male

1. So ma-ny pro - mi-ses_____ nev-er should be spo-
2. So ma-ny times_____ know I could have told_

Somethin' Stupid

Words & Music by C. Carson Parks

know I stand in line un - til you think you have the time to spend an
(2.) prac - tise ev - 'ry day to find some cle - ver lines to say to make the

drink or two.____
night's so blue.____ And

then I go and spoil it all____ by say - ing some - thing stu - pid like, "I

love_____ you."____ I can

see it in your eyes you still des - pise the same old lines you heard the

night be - fore._

And though it's just a line_ to you,_ for

me it's true and nev - er seemed so right be - fore._

D.S. al Coda

2. I

Coda

Lyrics:
The time is right, your per-fume fills my head, the stars get red and oh, the night's so blue._ And then I go and spoil it all_ by say-ing some-thing stu-pid like, "I love_ you."_ "I love_ you." "I

123456789